JOSEPH
& His Coat of Many Colors

Adapted by Tess Fries
Illustrated by Cheryl Mendenhall

JOSEPH & HIS COAT OF MANY COLORS
Published in 2006 by Spirit Press, an imprint of Dalmatian Press, LLC, Franklin, Tennessee
Copyright © 2006 Dalmatian Press, LLC.
All rights reserved

Art Directed by Shannon Osborne Thompson

ISBN: 1-40373-036-9 DP 1-40378-053-9 CE
CE10262-0806

Printed in the U.S.A.
06 07 08 09 NGS 10 9 8 7 6 5 4 3 2 1

Once there was an old man named Jacob who had twelve sons. Of all his sons, he loved Joseph the most. Jacob gave Joseph a special coat of bright and beautiful colors.

Joseph's brothers were very jealous, for they knew Joseph was their father's favorite son.

Joseph had two strange dreams about golden sheaves of grain and sparkling stars bowing down before him. His dreams meant that one day he would be greater than his brothers. His brothers were so angry! They couldn't believe that Joseph thought they would ever bow before him.

One day, Jacob asked Joseph to go and check on his brothers, who were many miles away taking care of their sheep and cattle. When Joseph's brothers saw him coming, they decided that they wanted to get rid of him, so that he would never rule over them.

Reuben, the oldest brother, didn't really want to hurt Joseph. He told his brothers to throw Joseph into a pit (so he could rescue him later). Joseph's brothers tore off his colorful coat and threw him into a deep, dark pit. Joseph begged his brothers to let him out. He was so afraid!

A short time later, while Reuben was gone, some traveling merchants came by—and the brothers got another idea. The brothers pulled Joseph from the pit and sold him to the merchants for twenty pieces of silver.

When they got home, they showed their father Joseph's coat and told him that wild animals had killed Joseph. Jacob cried because he thought Joseph was dead.

The merchants took Joseph to Egypt. He looked at the towering pyramids and the great Nile River and wondered what would happen to him. Maybe he worried that God had forgotten about him. But God was always with Joseph.

Joseph was sold
to a rich man
named Potiphar.
Potiphar liked
Joseph because
he was a hard
worker. Joseph
was cheerful
and always told
the truth.

One day, Potiphar had Joseph thrown into a prison. Potiphar thought Joseph had done something terrible, but he was innocent.

Joseph probably felt all alone in prison, but God was with him.

The butler and the baker for the Pharaoh of Egypt were in prison along with Joseph. One night they each had a scary dream. God helped Joseph tell them what their dreams meant.

Soon the butler went back to work for the Pharaoh. Two long years later, the Pharaoh had a strange dream. The butler remembered Joseph and thought he could help the Pharaoh understand his dream, so the Pharaoh sent for Joseph.

God helped Joseph explain the Pharaoh's dream. Joseph said, "God is showing you what He is going to do. For seven years there will be plenty of food for everyone. After that, there will be seven years with so little food that many people will starve." Joseph also told the Pharaoh how to save food now — so that there would be enough later.

The Pharaoh knew God had made Joseph wise, so he made Joseph second in command over all of Egypt. When Joseph rode through the streets, all the people bowed before him.

Joseph forgave his brothers for what they had done and invited his family to come live with him.

God did not
forget Joseph
when he was
scared and alone.
He gave him
courage and
comfort and
wisdom.

God knows
everything that
happens to
you, and
He will
not forget
you either.

Now [Jacob] loved Joseph more than any
of his other sons, because he had been
born to him in his old age; and he made
a richly ornamented robe for him.
Genesis 37:3
(NIV)